BESSIE SMITH

2

Bessie Smith

Photo by Edward Elcha,
New York, about 1924,
courtesy of Svend Holsoe.

BESSIE SMITH
EMPRESS OF THE BLUES

Compilation and Biography by Chris Albertson
Notes on Bessie Smith's Singing Style by Gunther Schuller
Musical Arrangements by George N. Terry
Edited by Clifford Richter

SCHIRMER BOOKS
A Division of Macmillan Publishing Co., Inc.
New York
COLLIER MACMILLAN PUBLISHERS
London

Bessie's Life

By Chris Albertson

Chattanooga, Tennessee—nestled in a bend of the Tennessee River—was settled as a trading post in 1828. Officially named ten years later, it prospered with the coming of railroads in the mid-nineteenth century and is today a small industrial city blanketed by air pollution that never seems to reach the homes of the well-to-do on Lookout and Signal Mountains.

It was from Chattanooga that General Sherman started his famous march on Atlanta and the sea, and it was there—thirty years later—that Bessie Smith first saw the light of day, April 15, 1894.

Bessie once described her first home as "a little ramshackle cabin;" it was actually a small one-room wooden shack on Charles Street at the foot of Cameron Hill, in an area of Chattanooga known as Blue Goose Hollow. There, in abject poverty and under unspeakable living conditions, William and Laura Smith brought seven children into the world.

Bessie's father—a part-time Baptist preacher—died while she was still an infant, and by the time she was eight or nine, Bessie's mother and two brothers had also passed.

The oldest daughter, Viola—herself the mother of an infant girl—raised her surviving brothers and sisters: Bessie, Tinnie, Lulu, Andrew, and Clarence in a tenement apartment on West Thirteenth Street in Chattanooga's Tannery Flats section. It was a rough neighborhood through which an air of hard times permeated. "Viola was a hard working woman," recalls a former neighbor. "She worked so hard taking care of them kids that she looked twenty years older than she was . . . I don't think she knew what it was like to party."

Actually, there was no time for partying and, having had a rather bitter experience with the father of her child, Viola had lost all interest in men. She took in washing to keep the household going and Clarence, now a teenager, supplemented the meager family income by taking whatever odd jobs he could get, but he had reached the age of restlessness, and, eager to explore the world beyond the limits of his hometown, he struck Viola a severe blow in 1904 when he joined a traveling minstrel troupe as a comedian. Clarence's sudden departure is said to have inspired Bessie to enter show business; accompanied by her brother Andrew on guitar, she began singing for small change on street corners.

Their main working area was a lively strip of Ninth Street which today remains Chattanooga's equivalent to Harlem's 125th Street—two blocks of chimerical gayety to which people escaped from the realities of the surrounding ghetto—but they were also frequently seen performing for the men who idled in front of the White Elephant, a popular bar at Thirteenth and Elm Streets. In good voice, even then, Bessie attracted attention with lyrics that sharply contrasted her youthful demeanor. As coins tinkled and rolled to rest at her feet, she would occasionally interrupt her song with a spirited response: "That's right Charlie, give to the church."

Despite the fact that she spent much of her time working in an adult milieu on the seamiest streets of Chattanooga, Bessie experienced a semblance of normal childhood: she attended the West Main Street School where she is believed to have gone as far as the eighth or ninth grade, and she found time to play with the neighborhood children, occasionally getting into mischief. Whenever this happened, Viola's punishment was to make Bessie spend the night in the outhouse. "I was raised in a shithouse," Bessie boasted in later years.

Some contemporaries recall that Bessie was often bullied by her playmates, a fact that may account for the extraordinary pugnacity she exhibited in her adult years. In any case, it seems clear that Bessie Smith was a very mature teenager when she left Chattanooga behind her, and that she was well equipped to deal with what lay ahead.

Her departure took place in 1912 when Clarence returned with the Moses Stokes troupe for a brief run at a Ninth Street storefront theatre. Already popular with the Ivory Theatre's amateur night audience, Bessie was ready to move on; after an audition arranged by Clarence, the Moses Stokes company left town with a new member.

The blues was strictly a man's music in the pre-war years when Bessie embarked on what was to be a lifelong road tour. It was the music of black minstrels who roamed the streets and country roads of the South and Southwest baring their souls for sustenance. Often physically handicapped, they usually accompanied themselves on stringed instruments and led a day to day existence that tended to inspire their poignant poetry.

Gertrude "Ma" Rainey was probably not the first woman to sing the blues, but she was certainly the first to become famous for breaking the tradition; not only did she sing the blues, but she took it off the streets and brought it before the footlights. Later to become known as the "Mother of the Blues," Ma Rainey was a short, portly woman with an infectious gold-toothed smile, a baby face and a style of singing that came closer to that of the male country blues singer than to the so-called "classic blues" style of other women who, like Bessie, followed in her footsteps.

Gertrude "Ma" Rainey, 1924 (Top) and Mamie Smith (1925). *Photos courtesy of Frank Driggs.*

It so happened that Ma Rainey was a member of the Moses Stokes company when Bessie joined it, and it is reasonable to assume that she inspired Bessie to include blues in her repertoire, but there is no truth to the widely believed story that Ma Rainey literally kidnaped Bessie and taught her everything she knew. "She may have taught her a few dance steps or showed her how to walk on stage," says veteran film actor Leigh Whipper, "but Bessie was born with that voice and she had a style of her own when I first heard her in Atlanta."

Whipper had first seen Bessie perform at Atlanta's "81" Theatre around 1913. She had only stayed with the Stokes troupe a few months and was now making the famous Atlanta theatre her home base as she toured with such companies as the Silas Green show and Pete Werley's Florida Blossoms.

Bessie's tours took her throughout the South, as far west as Muskogee, Oklahoma, and up the Eastern seaboard to Atlantic City, Baltimore and Philadelphia. At first she was buried in the chorus, but by 1918 she had teamed up with another singer, Hazel Green, for a specialty act, and soon thereafter she had gained sufficient popularity to go it on her own.

It was during those early years on the road that Bessie married a Mississippian by the name of Earl Love, but details of their relationship remain obscure for Bessie seemed reluctant to discuss him except to say that he died long before 1922 when she made Philadelphia her home.

The following year, as Americans faced their third year of Prohibition, Bessie's life and career were to be changed radically when an embryonic record industry and a Philadelphia night watchman made bids for her.

For two decades, the record industry virtually ignored the existence of black people, both as artists and as consumers. Black composers had for several years turned out hit tunes that caught the fancy of white America, but they were always recorded by white artists until 1920 when Fred Hager of Okeh took a chance on Mamie Smith, a black vaudeville singer from Ohio.

It was Mamie Smith's second release, *Crazy Blues*, that really jolted the industry. With over a hundred thousand copies sold in the first month of its release, *Crazy Blues* demonstrated the commercial value of black talent and started a blues boom that had talent scouts combing black-populated parts of the country for women who sang the blues. Suddenly there appeared to be an abundance of such women, but, as it turned out, most of them were overnight converts from pop or church music who learned the *form* but lacked the *feel* of the blues idiom.

Bessie was soon to rise above all her contemporaries, even Ma Rainey, but her early record auditions did not fare well: Bessie sounded too black for Thomas Edison, "voice—N.G.," he wrote opposite her name in his ledger; "too rough," said Fred Hager after hearing her Okeh test recording.

Thus Bessie had to wait until 1923 before Frank Walker of Columbia Records, acting on a suggestion from a Philadelphia record dealer, sent pianist Clarence Williams to "find her and bring her back up here."

On February 15, 1923, Bessie, accompanied by Clarence Williams, recorded *Down Hearted Blues* and *Gulf Coast Blues* at Columbia's studio on New York's Columbus Circle. According to Frank Walker, who would supervise all of Bessie's records for the next eight years, "She looked like anything *but* a singer; she looked about seventeen, tall and fat and scared to death—just awful!"

Columbia Records publicity photo, 1923.

Scared or not, the record was a sensational hit with 780,000 copies sold in the first six months. All Bessie ever made from that first record was $125, but it quickly established her as the leading blues singer and it wasn't long before plans were being made for the first Bessie Smith touring company.

Prior to making the record, Bessie had met and fallen in love with Jack Gee, an illiterate night watchman with business acumen powered by greed. Their marriage, June 7, coincided with the release of *Down Hearted Blues*, and both events were to have a profound effect on Bessie's life: the record and subsequent releases sky-rocketed her to fame, made her the highest paid black entertainer of her day, and drew her into a whirlwind of work with a schedule most people could not survive; the marriage, a union of two strong-willed people with disparate life styles, brought her moments of happiness, but it wasn't long before the novelty wore off and a masochistic cat and mouse game unfolded.

At first, Jack took a deep interest in his wife's affairs. He quit his ill-paid night watchman's job, went on the road with Bessie, and was instrumental in her getting more money for her work. A new deal with Columbia gave her $200 per issued selection (but still no royalties) and she was soon commanding as much as $2000 per week for her theatre appearances.

Those early days of her marriage and widespread fame were happy days for Bessie. She bought Jack three-hundred-dollar suits and arranged for her shows to go under the banner "Jack Gee presents," but everyone knew that Jack was in reality Mr. Bessie Smith, and this soon began to affect their relationship.

As Bessie entered her third year of super stardom, her marriage began to deteriorate. With increasing frequency, Jack began to take leave of the show while on the road, giving Bessie an excuse to go on a spree consisting of heavy drinking and sexual promiscuity that embraced both sexes. It became a pattern with Jack returning at the least expected moment, the two having it out physically, and Bessie going into a period of sobriety.

"When her and Jack were on good terms," recalls Ruby Walker, Jack's niece who spent fourteen years on the road as one of Bessie's chorus girls and a close companion, "you couldn't pay her to touch a drop, but when they had their fights she really carried on—she would drink like mad. You see, Jack was so conservative that you couldn't ball with him. He was so strict and he wasn't in Bessie's life at all—he was all right for her when she felt like being quiet, and no drinking, just a wife, a homebody. But when it came to a good time, and she got those spells and wanted to go off, Jack wasn't the one for her. That's why she always had to go and mess with the young people, those who were of her breed, those who could keep up with her.

"She was a strong woman with a beautiful strong constitution, and she loved a good time. And she knew every joint—I don't know *how* that woman knew so many joints, but she could take you into more beat up places, honey. She was strictly show business: sitting around was all right for a month or so, but that's as far as she could go without *going out and clowning*. She would go out, stay two or three weeks, ball, and then be ready to keep quiet for a month or so. Then Jack would come in handy, but Jack couldn't see it that way, that's why every time you looked he was knocking her down, or catching her *going out of a place or coming into a place*."

Bessie and Jack continued to run their game of tag, but each fulfilled the other's need: Bessie needed Jack's sobering presence to balance her scales while he, having acquired an addictive taste for show business glamor and relative wealth, needed her to sate a growing appetite.

Just as Bessie's private life had developed a pattern, so had her work schedule. She would take a well-rehearsed troupe to Atlanta in the spring, lease a railroad car and zig-zag throughout the South with her tent show until Labor Day, making one and two-night stops in small towns and hamlets. Then, with an augmented troupe, she spent the winter months on the T.O.B.A. (Theatre Owner's Booking Association) circuit of black theatres, playing one or two weeks in each city from New Orleans to Detroit.

By 1924 Bessie had become the highest-paid black entertainer in the country, and had been proclaimed the Empress of the Blues. The following summer she added real class to her tours by purchasing her own railroad car. Seventy-eight feet long, it could accommodate the whole show with seven staterooms comfortably sleeping twenty-eight of the more privileged performers, and a lower level that housed as many as thirty-five additional troupers. The galley and bathroom featured hot and cold running water, which was something most T.O.B.A. (popularly referred to as "Tough On Black Asses") theatres couldn't even offer, and a room in the rear of the car stored the electric generator used to light up Bessie's tent, the huge canvas and cases of soft drinks,

Jack Gee, *from the files of Frank Music Corp.*

Crackerjacks, peanuts and other items sold by Bessie's crew doubling as vendors. The tent's long center pole rested in a corridor which ran the length of the car.

While her show was on the road, Bessie made frequent trips to New York City for the purpose of recording. Her Columbia contracts only called for her to do twelve selections annually, but she had made a hundred recordings by December of 1925, the end of her third year with the Company (including four duets with a rival, Clara Smith, the most successful of which, *My Man Blues*, is included in this collection). Low as her financial recompense was for these efforts, Bessie regarded her recordings as promotional tools that filled her tent with whites as well as blacks, and had people lining up for blocks in front of theatres that boasted her appearance.

In fact, Bessie's shows were so well attended that theatre owners cut them short in order to create a fast turnover. This meant that she often had to put on as many as ten shows a day, seven days a week. To unwind from such a grueling schedule, Bessie, in Jack's absence, would drink huge amounts of corn liquor and surround herself with people who shared her lack of inhibitions, but no matter how drunk she got, Bessie made sure she controlled the situation.

Her sprees often began with her walking into a speakeasy, slamming a hundred dollar bill on the bar and demanding "Give everybody a drink, don't let nobody in and don't let nobody out." Then she would bask in the crowd, relate some humorous gossip recently learned, pick an appropriate entourage and move on to some other place.

Bessie never acted the super star. She wore expensive fur coats and jewelry when the occasion called for it, but she much preferred to dress plainly and be amongst what she called her "own people," friends who accepted her as a person. She abhorred status seekers, particularly blacks who sought an entree to white upper class society; not that she disliked whites, but she saw acculturation as a curse. "My hair is kinky, but my man don't care; any man's a fool to want a woman for her hair," she wrote in her lyrics to *Sweet Black Woman*, a song she never got around to recording.

In an era when many blacks sought white acceptance by adopting their mannerisms, speech and life-style, Bessie often went out of her way to emphasize her blackness. In 1928, when Carl Van Vechten, the noted author and photographer, invited her to a party of society page figures, Bessie rebelled against the bejeweled crowd of patronizing whites and their black pets by throwing her hostess, actress Fania Marinoff Van Vechten, to the floor and showering her with choice expletives. Her rebellion carried over to the next afternoon when, clad in an ermine coat, she gave an impromptu performance for "her people," seated on a garbage can amid the trash in an alley behind the Lafayette Theatre where she was headlining.

Such behavior helped to endear Bessie to millions of followers; they found it hard to identify with the likes of Josephine Baker and Ethel Waters, stars who hob-nobbed with European royalty and sang songs aimed at another culture. Bessie's blues, on the other hand, told real stories of real people like themselves, and Bessie—who could well afford to live in the relative splendor of Merrick Park, a Long Island community of well-to-do blacks—rarely displayed the trimmings that come with fame. Bessie sang of mean mistreaters and two-timing husbands, offered advice to the dejected, and made it quite clear that she herself was not immune to such problems. Occasionally she borrowed a song from Tin Pan Alley, but only if the lyrics—which she often altered to suit her needs—had the ring of truth. "I don't ever remember any artist in all my long, long years—and this goes back to some of the famous singers, including Billie Holiday—who could evoke the response from her listeners that Bessie did," recalled the late Frank Schiffman, who frequently booked Bessie for the Lafayette and Apollo theatres. "Whatever pathos there is in the world, whatever sadness she had, was brought out in her singing—and the audience knew it and responded to it."

In 1926, Bessie saw two long-time dreams come true: she moved her three sisters, her niece and two nephews from Chattanooga and situated them comfortably in two Philadelphia houses; she adopted a six-year-old boy whom she named Jack Gee, Jr. Neither event pleased Jack, but Bessie softened him up with the gift of a specially-built Cadillac car, which he eventually gambled away.

Throughout the twenties, Bessie continued to tour, draw huge crowds and make records. By the spring of 1929, she had contributed fifty more selections to Columbia's so-called "race" catalogue, but sales had now tapered off considerably and with the talkies slowly killing vaudeville, the handwriting was on the wall.

(Cont. p. 16)

Jack Gee, Jr., 1937. *Photo courtesy of Chris Albertson.*

DOUGLAS
~Gilmor Theàtre~

GILMOR STREET NEAR SARATOGA

PROGRAM FOR NEXT WEEK
——VAUDEVILLE——
Ralph—HARRIS & FATIMA—Alda
In their Latest "WHO IS WHO"

HOLMES & EDWARDS
The Crazy Man and the Maid

Hazel—GREEN & SMITH--Bessie

Hip Ha Hip Ha Girls.   Men here is a chance for a Good Wife
HIRAM SORRELL AND LITTLE TOM. By request of the public

——Special Feature Pictures——
Changed Daily.   Showing all the Latest Serials.
The only Vaudeville and Motion Picture Parlor owned and managed
exclusively by colored people.
Vaudeville changed Monday and Thursday

First Show at 7.30   Second Show at 9.30

Electric Fans and Exhaust Ventilator assuring comfort to our Patro

HIRAM SORRELL, Manager   GEORGE DOUGLAS,

LAFAYETTE THEATRE

This Week, Thurs., Fri., Sat., Sun., Sept. 25, 26, 27, 28

CONTINUOUS DAILY FROM 2 TO 11

| EXTRA ATTRACTION | THE GREATEST AND HIGHEST SALARIED Race STAR IN THE WORLD | EXTRA ATTRACTION |

THE EMPRESS OF BLUES SINGERS

BESSIE SMITH

In conjunction with the above Great Star
FOUR COMEDY KINGS
BILLY KING   BILLY HIGGINS
DO DOE GREEN   MARSHALL RODGERS
In the Big MUSICAL COMEDY
"THE POLITICIANS"
and a Bunch of Pretty Girls

15c-25c   25c-35c-50c

Don't Forget the Big MIDNIGHT SHOW FRIDAY
Seats will be reserved for the Midnight Show only
Order your Seat now and get your choice

Coming Monday, September 29
King's Musical Comedy "OVER THE TOP," with
ng. Billy Higgins, Marshall Rodgers and Bunch of

While more polished singers like Ethel Waters and Alberta Hunter appealed to white audiences and entertained European royalty, Bessie's tours never took her farther east than Long Island. (Photo of Ethel Waters on opposite page is a rare 1933 pose used by Carl Van Vechten on personal post cards—courtesy of Hank Berrings; photo of Alberta Hunter, above, shows her standing second from left in a scene from her own 1934 revue in Paris—*photo courtesy of Miss Hunter.*

Bessie and Jack in happier days. Photo by Blum, Philadelphia, *from the files of Frank Music Corp.*

Critics such as Brooks Atkinson and Richard Lockridge lauded her performance in "Pansy," a black musical which opened on Broadway in mid-May, 1929, but they declared the show a disaster and Bessie's Broadway debut ended after three performances. Her film debut in a short called "St. Louis Blues," made the following month, was more successful, but the stock market crash in October reduced the roar of the decade to a whimper, and the glory that had been Bessie's in the twenties was never hers again.

Bessie's personal life had suffered a crash of its own that year with her discovery that Jack had used some of her money to finance a show starring Gertrude Saunders, a pseudo-operatic pop singer whom he was also having an affair with. Bessie could possibly have tolerated Jack's outside love interest, but his use of her money for a rival show was more than she could take. Her reaction was prompt: immediately following a performance in Cincinnati, she stepped into a cab, costume and all, and rode to Columbus where Jack was stopping with Gertrude Saunders' show. There, in a small hotel room, Bessie and Jack ended their relationship in physical combat that left the room a shambles.

As the country plunged into the Great Depression, Bessie picked up the pieces of her life and began shaping a new one with Richard Morgan, a long-time friend from Birmingham who had achieved considerable success as a Chicago bootlegger. Richard was a handsome, mild-mannered man with a winning personality and an obvious love for Bessie. "It was obvious that Bessie and my uncle were very devoted to each other," says Lionel Hampton, Morgan's nephew, "and I don't believe there was anything he wouldn't do for her."

Unlike Jack, Richard Morgan felt at home in a show business milieu. A renowned party giver, he had entertained virtually every black performer who came through Chicago during the twenties and he was right in step with Bessie when it came to having a good time.

Richard became Bessie's manager during a difficult period when she began playing to half-empty houses for a fraction of her previous fee, but he would often make up for losses out of his own pocket, and together they weathered the storm.

Gertrude Saunders, photo by Edward Elcha, *courtesy of Frank Driggs.*

Bessie rarely saw Jack, except when they fought over custody of their adopted son—it was a battle which Bessie eventually lost, and the boy spent most of his early teens in orphanages. "Mama wanted me to have an education, she said she'd give me clothes, a car, anything, if only I'd go to school," recalls Jack, Jr. "I didn't listen to her, I just kept running away."

Columbia dropped Bessie from its roster of artists in 1931, but not, as has been asserted, because blues records were no longer marketable. The fact is that no records were selling well, and executives like Frank Walker saw little hope for the future of the industry. It is, of course, true that blues were not the sort of thing people wanted to hear during the Depression years, but Bessie fully realized this and she had no intention of becoming a relic.

Bessie's repertoire had always stretched beyond blues limits and she still possessed the most powerful voice in the land, so she did not find it difficult to translate her artistry into the new language of swing music. Singing songs like *Smoke Gets In Your Eyes* and *Tea For Two*, Bessie shed her elaborate costumes and headgear in favor of simple evening gowns. Gone, too, were the wigs she had worn throughout the twenties; her hair was now close-cropped and swept back—she looked more striking than ever.

In 1933 she returned to the recording studio to make four selections for the Okeh label. These, her final recordings, give us a hint of the transition that was taking place in Bessie's music, but we will unfortunately never hear how she sounded by the mid-thirties when, as Lionel Hampton has put it, "Bessie was right in there, ready to become a national figure with the rest of us in the swing era."

By mid-1937 Bessie had begun to stage a remarkable comeback. A new audience cheered her for twelve weeks at Connie's Inn on Broadway, popular swing era figures courted her and there was talk of more records—with such accompanists as Count Basie and Benny Goodman—a Hollywood film, and a Carnegie Hall appearance.

It all might have happened, but in the dark, early morning hours of September 26, 1937, as Richard Morgan drove Bessie to Clarksdale, Mississippi from an engagement in Memphis, their car struck the rear of a National Biscuit Company truck. Bessie's injuries were fatal; she died later that morning at the age of forty-three, but the Empress had lived a hundred years.

Bessie, a detailed book-length biography of Bessie Smith by Chris Albertson, was published in January, 1973 by Stein & Day, New York.

The Empress lies in state, October 1937.
Photo from Philadelphia Tribune.

Photo, about 1920, *courtesy of Rudi Blesh.*

Photo, 1923, by Edward Elcha, *courtesy of Rudi Blesh.*

Photo, 1923,
by Edward Elcha,
courtesy of Jerome Ford.

Photo, 1924, by Edward Elcha,
courtesy of Frank Driggs.

"SORROWFUL BLUES"
Hear **Bessie Smith** *sob it on*
RECORD 14020 D
then listen to the other side
"ROCKING CHAIR BLUES"

Having a phonograph without these records is like having ham without eggs

From Columbia Records ads, 1924.

Photo, 1924, by Edward Elcha, *courtesy of Frank Driggs.*

From the 1929 Film *ST. LOUIS BLUES.*
Photos courtesy of Rudi Blesh.

Trucking for Carl Can Vechten, 1936, *photos courtesy of Chris Albertson.*

Photo, 1936, by Carl Van Vechten,
courtesy of Chris Albertson.

Photo 1936 by Carl Van Vechten,
courtesy of Chris Albertson.

Photo, 1936, by Carl Van Vechten, *courtesy of Chris Albertson.*

The Last Curtain Rings Down For Bessie Smith

A segment of the 8,000 persons that thronged the streets outside of the O. V. Catto Elks Home, 16th and Fitzwater Sts., Philadelphia, to pay tribute to the great blues singer who met her death as the result of an automobile accident. The above photo shows the casket being carried from the auditorium for transportation to the cemetery.

Bessie's tombstone, gift of Janis Joplin and Juanita Green. Photo taken at the dedication, August 7, 1970. *Courtesy of Columbia Records.*

Bessie's Singing Style

By Gunther Schuller

As early as *Jailhouse Blues* (September 1923) we can hear the embellishment traits that form the essence of Bessie's style. In the first line after the scene-setting introduction, "Thirty days in jail with my back turned to the wall," the importance of the words in the sentence determines the degree of embellishment each receives. Almost every word is emphasized by an upward scoop or slide, but each one differently. The words "thirty," "jail," and "wall"—the three main words of the sentence— are also those most modified by slides. "Thirty" starts with a relatively fast upward slur from approximately *e* flat to *g* flat. (The piece is in the key of *e* flat. All pitches are approximate, since Bessie moves fairly freely within the microtonal subdivisions of the scale.) "Days" slides more slowly from the blue flat-third to the major-third, *g*. The next word, "in," is a slightly flat *g*, in preparation for a large major-third upward scoop on "jail": the most important word, *ergo* the strongest embellishment.

These four elements are now reused, but with different words, of course, and in a different sequence: a flat *g* for "with," and *e* flat for "my," a minor-third slide on "back" (similar to "thirty"), and a longer *g* flat to *g* slur on the word "turned." In the sense that "with my" is similar to "in jail"—the only difference being that the final return to *g* in "jail" is not consummated on "my"— we have here a reshuffling of four degrees of slides from the initial order of 1, 2, 3, 4 to 3, 4, 1, 2. The next two words, "to the," transitional and less important, are appropriately unembellished *g*'s, rhythmically short and connective.

So far all embellishments have been upward slides. Now, on "wall" Bessie uses one of her other frequently employed ornamental devices, a double slide which at first descends to a final pitch. Here, in *Jailhouse Blues*, because Bessie is heading for the tonic, the approximate sliding pitches are [shown in example A]. (Bessie used two other variants of this embellishment. Another one, also on the tonic, was [example B], a quick downward dip to the sixth of the chord and up again. It is used, for example on the word "wall" in the repeat of the first line of *Jailhouse Blues*. But her most frequently used double-note ornament was reserved for the third of the chord [example C]. This latter ornament appears with great consistency starting around 1925, and can be heard on

any number of recordings: *Reckless Blues, Sobbin' Hearted Blues, Cold in Hand Blues*, and many others).

On the word "wall" in the repeat line, we encounter another of Bessie's favorite devices, a phrase-ending "drop-off" or "fall-off." It is usually associated with the tonic and drops quickly to the sixth of the scale [example D]. But occasionally she did similar "drop-offs" on the third and even on the fifth of the key, as in *Cold in Hand Blues*, where the "fall-off" drops to the third [example E].

Two further phrase idiosyncrasies appear in *Jailhouse Blues*. The one is a variant of the "drop-off," longer and more pitch-inflected. We hear it here on the word "turned," an interpolated phrase repeating the last of the first line as a fill-in. (This two-bar "fill-in" would normally have been an instrumental response to the singer's first line, but since *Jailhouse Blues* was accompanied only by a pianist, Clarence Williams, Bessie occasionally decided to fill in the two bars herself.) On the word "turned" she sings [example F], thus turning the word into a blues moan. Here, although the pitches are still connected by slides, they are nevertheless more articulated than in her other ornaments so that an actual melodic motive emerges.

Bessie also had a unique ability to break phrases into unexpected segments and to breathe at such phrase interruptions, without in the slightest impairing overall continuity, textual or melodic. In the repeat of the "Thirty days" line, Bessie breathes twice at unexpected places: between the word "my" and "back" for a real break in the phrase; then again between "turned" and "to the wall," a smaller interruption. The reason for these breath breaks is the previously mentioned interpolated half-phrase, "turned to the wall," which prevented her from going to the end of the second repeat line without breathing. Thus the overall partitioning of both lines is as follows (' is an incidental breath mark, * is a more pronounced interruption):

Thirty days in jail' with my back turned' to the wall'
Turned* to the wall/
Thirty days in jail with my* back turned' to the wall.
Note that in the one place where one might have expected a breath, marked /, Bessie goes right on, bridging the natural division of the sentence.

One could cite hundreds of such examples in which word and melodic patterns are broken up in unexpected and often asymmetrical ways. It should suffice to cite one more, the fourth chorus of *Cold in Hand Blues* (not counting the opening verse). Note the breath interruptions here too, the first time after the word "myself," the second time *in the middle of the word*, yet without the slightest loss of continuity. (The trumpet responses are by Louis Armstrong.)

THE ABOVE is an excerpt from the chapter on Bessie Smith in *Early Jazz*, by Gunther Schuller (Oxford University Press, 1968). The entire chapter is highly recommended to those seriously interested in Bessie Smith's work. *Jailhouse Blues* is included in this collection (page 39).

(WOKE UP) COLD IN HAND
Words and Music by Jazz Gillum
© Copyright 1962 by Leeds Music Corporation
All Rights Reserved   Used By Permission

From the files of Frank Music Corp.

Original manuscript for "Pickpocket Blues", possibly in Bessie Smith's or Fred Longshaw's handwriting, but certainly the sheet Bessie worked from when she recorded it in February, 1928.

Carl Van Vechten
Photo

It Makes My Love Come Down

Words and Music by
BESSIE SMITH

2. Wild about my toodle-oh.
   When I gets my toodle-oh
   It makes my love come down. Want ev'ry poun'.
   Hear me cryin', it makes my love come down.

3. Likes my coffee, likes my tea,
   Daffy about my stingaree.
   It makes my love come down. I wanna be aroun'.
   Oh, Sweet Papa, it makes my love come down.

4. If you want to hear me rave
   Honey, give me what I crave.
   It makes my love come down. Actin' like a clown.
   Can't help from braggin', it makes my love come down.

5. Come on and be my desert Sheik.
   You're so strong and I'm so weak.
   It makes my love come down, to be love-land bound.
   Red Hot Papa, it makes my love come down.

6. If you want me for your own
   Kiss me nice or leave me alone.
   It makes my love come down, it makes my love come down.
   Take me bye-bye, it makes my love come down.

7. When you take me for a ride
   When I'm close up by your side,
   It makes my love come down, ridin' all aroun'.
   Easy ridin' makes my love come down.

Long Road*

Words and Music by
BESSIE SMITH

Slow blues

mf

mp

Eb   Ab9   Ab7   Eb A° Fm7 Eb

1. It's a long old road,   but I'm gon-na find — the end; _____

Eb7   Ab9   Ab7

— It's a long old road, _____ but I'm gon-na find — the

*Also known as Long Old Road.

3. Weepin' and cryin', tears fallin' on the groun',
   Weepin' and cryin', tears fallin' on the groun',
   When I got to the end I was so worried down.

4. Picked up my bag, baby, and I tried it again.
   Picked up my bag, baby, and I tried it again.
   I got to make it, I've got to find the end.

5. You can't trust nobody, you might as well be alone,
   You can't trust nobody, you might as well be alone,
   Found my long lost friend and I might as well stayed at home.

Jailhouse Blues

Words and Music by
BESSIE SMITH
and **CLARENCE WILLIAMS**

Spoken: Lord this house is gonna get raided! Yes, sir!

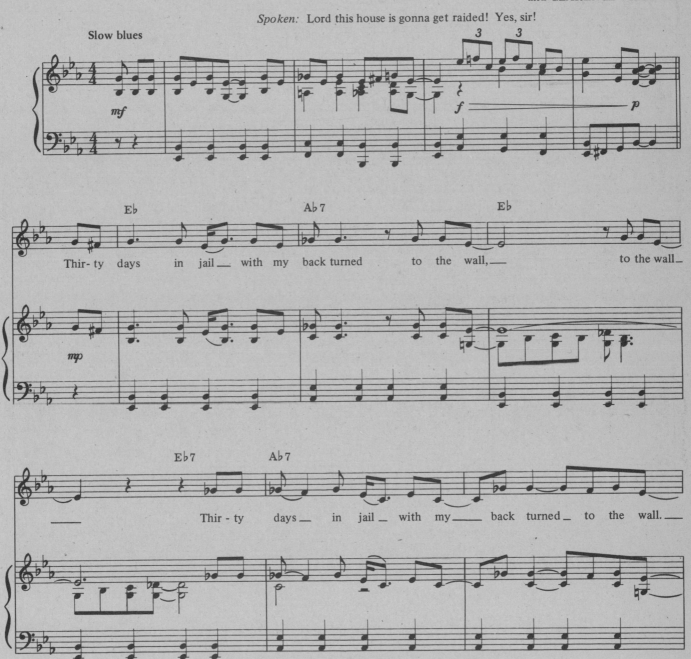

2. You better stop your man from ticklin' me under my chin, under my chin,
   You better stop your man from ticklin' me under my chin,
   'Cause if he keeps on ticklin' I'm sure gonna take him on in.

3. Good mornin' blues, blues how do you do? How do you do?
   Good mornin' blues, blues how do you do?
   Well, I just come here to have a few words with you.

Dirty No-Gooder's Blues

Words and Music by
BESSIE SMITH

1. Did you ev-er fall___ in love___ with a man___ that was no good?___

Did you ev-er fall___ in love___ with a man___ that is no

good?_____ No mat-ter what you did for him, he nev-er un-der-stood.

2. The meanest things he could say would thrill you through and through,
   The meanest things he could say would thrill you through and through,
   And there wasn't nothin' too dirty for that man to do.

3. He'd treat you nice and kind till he win your heart and hand,
   He'd treat you nice and kind till he win your heart and hand,
   Then he git so cruel that man you just could not stand.

4. Lawd, I really don't think no man's love can last,
   Lawd, I don't think no man's love can last;
   They'll love you to death then treat you like a thing of the past.

5. There's nineteen men livin' in my neighborhood,
   There's nineteen men livin' in my neighborhood,
   Eighteen of them are fools and the one ain't no doggone good.

6. Lawd, Lawd, Lawd, Lawd, Lawd, Lawd, Lawd,
   Lawd, ..., Lawd, Lawd, Lawd, Lawd,
   That dirty no-good man treats me just like I'm a dog.

Down In The Dumps

Words by
LEOLA P. WILSON

Music by
WESLEY WILSON

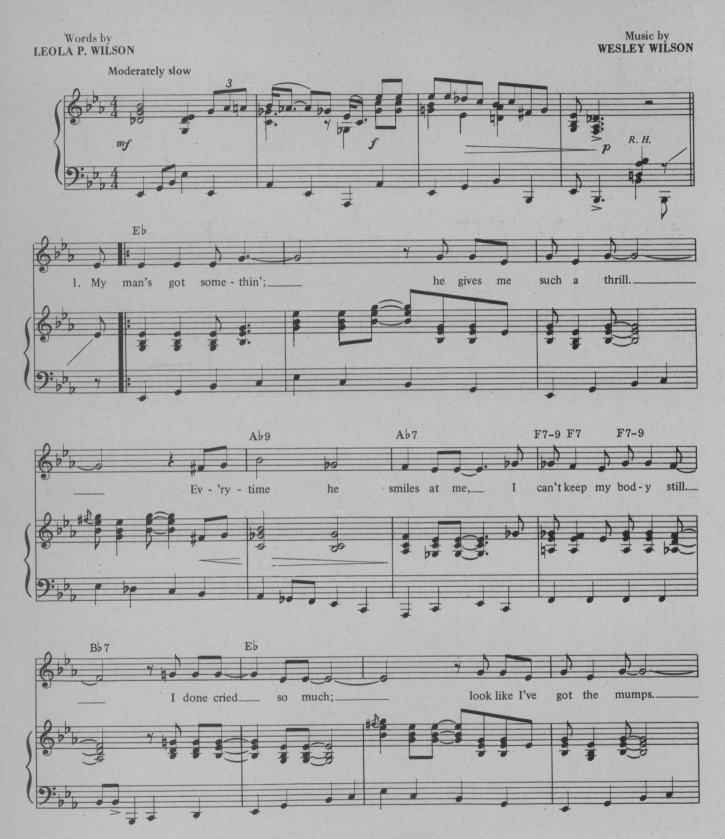

1. My man's got some-thin'; ___ he gives me such a thrill. ___

___ Ev-'ry-time he smiles at me, ___ I can't keep my bod-y still. ___

I done cried ___ so much; ___ look like I've got the mumps. ___

2. I had a nightmare last night, when I laid down.

   When I woke up this mornin', my sweet man couldn't be found.

   I'm goin' down to the river; into it I'm goin' to jump.

   Can't keep from worryin' 'cause I'm down in the dumps.

3. Some one knocked on my door last night when I was asleep.

   I thought it was that sweet man of mine makin' his 'fore day creep.

   Wasn't nothin' but my landlord, a great big chump.

   Stay 'way from my door Mr. Landlord, 'cause I'm down in the dumps.

4. When I woke up my pillow was wet with tears.

   Just one day from that man o' mine seems like a thousand years.

   But I'm gonna straighten up, straighter than Andy Gump.

   Ain't no use of me tellin' that lie 'cause I'm down in the dumps.

5. I'm twenty-five years old, that ain't no old maid.

   I got plenty of vim and vitality, I'm sure that I can make the grade.

   I'm always like a tiger, I'm ready to jump.

   I need a whole lots of lovin' 'cause I'm down in the dumps.

In The House Blues

Words and Music by
BESSIE SMITH

in' to my win-dow, an' look-in' out of my door. Walk-

in' to my win-dow, an' look-in' out of my door.

Wish-in' that my man would come home once more.

2. Can't
3. Ketch

2. Can't eat, can't sleep, so weak I can't walk my floor.
Can't eat, can't sleep, so weak I can't walk my floor.
Feel like hollerin' murder, let the Police Squad get me once more.

They woke me before day with trouble on my mind.
They woke me before day with trouble on my mind.
Wringin' my hands and screamin', walkin' the floor hollerin' and cryin'.

3. Catch 'em, don't let them blues in here.
Catch 'em, don't let them blues in here.
They shakes me in my bed, can't set down in my chair.

Oh, the blues has got me on the go.
Oh, they've got me on the go.
They runs around my house, in and out of my front door.

Shipwreck Blues

Words and Music by
BESSIE SMITH

Safety Mamma

Words and Music by
BESSIE SMITH

Take Me For A Buggy Ride

Words by
LEOLA P. WILSON

Music by
WESLEY WILSON

Moderately slow

Refrain:

Dad-dy, you real-ly knows your stuff when you take me for___ a bug-gy ride.
Dad-dy, you're as sweet as you can be when you take me for___ a bug-gy ride.

I like you when you got your hab-its on;___ you can shift your gear___ with so much
When you set me down up-on your knee,___ and ask me___ to be your

pride.___ I gets a fun-ny feel-in' when you gaze in-to my eyes. You
bride.___ When you hug and kiss me it makes me feel fine.___ I

Blue Blues

Words and Music by
BESSIE SMITH

Lis - ten to my sto - ry, an'
You done lis - ten to, my sto - ry, an'

ev - 'ry - thing 'll come out true.
ev - 'ry - thing come out true.

1. *To next strain*

2. *Fine*

Fine

When your man is gone, your

rent is all due,___ he's not com - in' back,___ you know he's all thru.

Wasted Life Blues

Words and Music by
BESSIE SMITH

2. No father to guide me, no mother to care,
   Must bear my troubles all alone.
   Not even a brother to help me share
   This burden I must bear alone.
      Refrain

3. I'm settin' and thinkin' of the days gone by,
   They filled my heart with pain.
   I'm too weak to stand and too strong to cry,
   But I'm forgittin' it all in vain.
      Refrain

4. I've traveled and wandered almost everywhere
   To git a little joy from life.
   Still I've gained nothin' but wars and despair,
   Still strugglin' in this world of strife.
      Refrain

Standin' In The Rain Blues

Words and Music by
BESSIE SMITH

68

Squeeze Me

Words and Music by
THOMAS "FATS" WALLER
and **CLARENCE WILLIAMS**

Baby Won't You Please Come Home

Words and Music by
CHARLES WARFIELD and
CLARENCE WILLIAMS

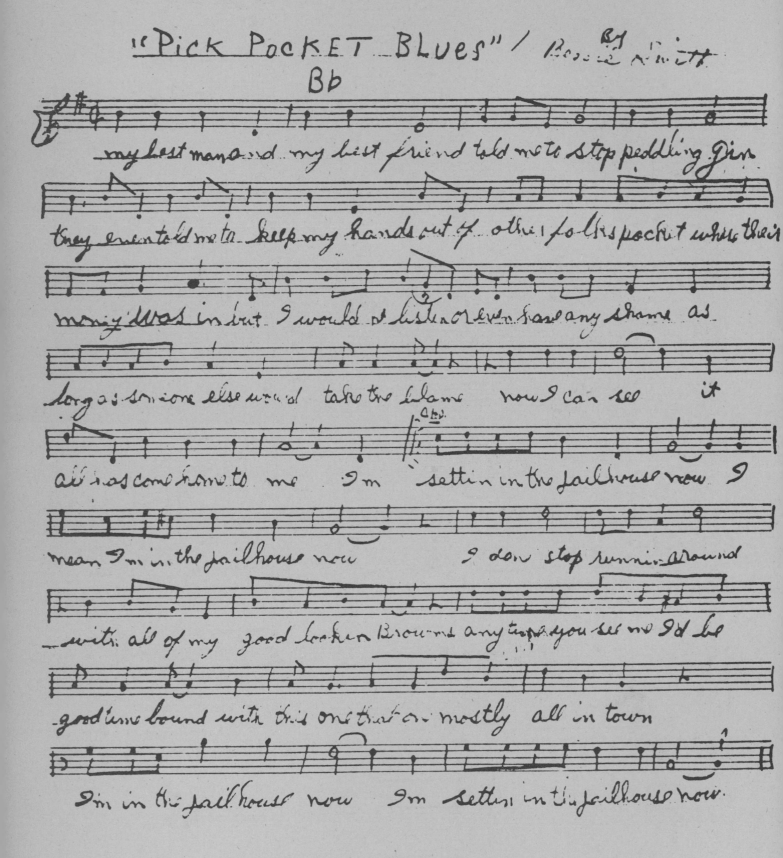

Pickpocket Blues

Words and Music by
BESSIE SMITH

have an-y shame___ long as some-one else would take the blame.___

Now ___ I can see it all come home to me. I'm

set-tin' in the jail-house now,___ I mean, I'm in the jail-house

now. I ___ done stop___ run-nin' a-round___ { 1. with
{ 2. with

79

Backwater Blues

Words and Music by
BESSIE SMITH

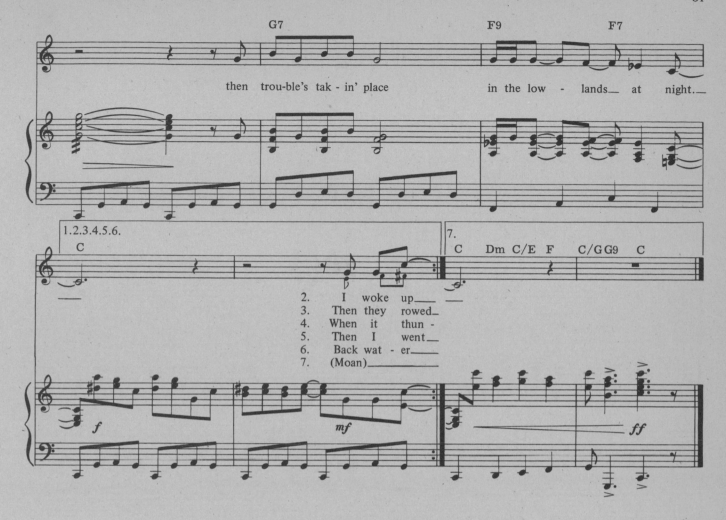

then trou-ble's tak-in' place   in the low - lands__ at   night.__

1.2.3.4.5.6.   7.

2.   I woke up__ __
3.   Then they   rowed__
4.   When it   thun -
5.   Then I   went__
6.   Back wat - er____
7.   (Moan)_____

(2) I woke up this mornin', can't even get out of my door
     I woke up this mornin', can't even get out of my door
     That's enough trouble to make a poor girl wonder where she want to go.

(3) Then they rowed a little boat about five miles 'cross the farm.
     Then they rowed a little boat about five miles 'cross the farm.
     I packed all my clothes, throwed them in and they rowed me along.

(4) When it thunders and lightnin', and the wind begins to blow,
     When it thunders and lightnin', and the wind begins to blow,
     There's thousands of people ain't got no place to go.

(5) Then I went and stood upon some high old lonesome hill.
     Then I went and stood upon some high old lonesome hill.
     Then looked down on the house where I used to live.

(6) Back-water blues done caused me to pack my things and go.
     Back-water blues done caused me to pack my things and go.
     'Cause my house fell down and I can't live there no more.

(7) (Moan)- - - - - - - - - -I can't move no more,
     (Moan)- - - - - - - - -I can't move no more,
     There ain't no place for a poor old girl to go.

Young Woman's Blues

Words and Music by
BESSIE SMITH

Woke up this morn-in' when chick-ens was crow-in' for day.

Felt on the right side of my pil - la, my man had gone a-

way.

By his pil - la

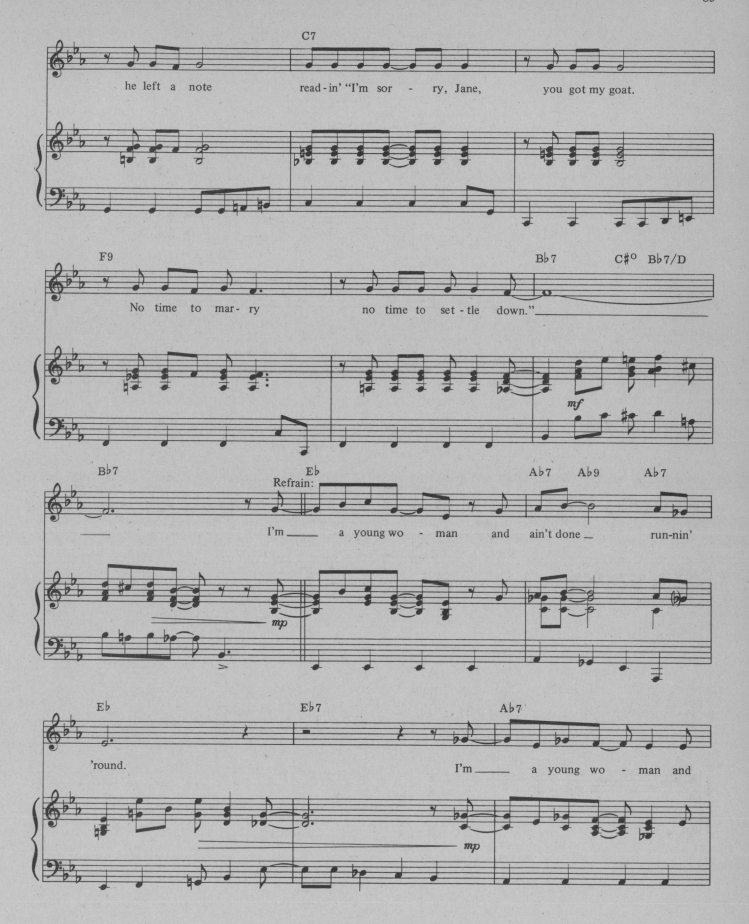

ain't done _____ run-nin''round ____

Some peo-ple

call ____ me a ho-bo, ____ Some call ____ me a bum. No-bod-y knows my name,_ no-bod-y

knows what I've done. __

I'm as good__ as an-y wo-man__ in__ your

town.

I _____ ain't no high yel-la,

See If I'll Care

Words and Music by
CLARENCE WILLIAMS
and *ALEX HILL*

New Orleans Hop Scop Blues

Words and Music by
GEORGE W. THOMAS

Nobody Knows You
When You're Down And Out

Words and Music by
JIMMIE COX

Baby Doll

Words and Music by
BESSIE SMITH

Moderately Slow Blues

Verse:

Hon-ey, there's a fun-ny feel-ing 'round my heart, and it's bound to drive your ma-ma wild It must be some-thing they call the Cu-ban doll. It weren't your ma - ma's an-gel child. I

hard luck Bes - sie, dog - gone your bad luck soul.____ I want to be some - bod - y's ba - by doll so I can get____ my lov - ing____ all the time, I mean____ to get my lov - ing all____ the time.____

Please Help Me Get Him Off My Mind

Words and Music by
BESSIE SMITH

kicked and dogged me 'round;_____ And when I try_____ to kill him that's when my love for him____ comes down.____

2. I've
3. It
4. Gyp - sy

2. I've come to see you gypsy, beggin' on my bended knees,
   I've come to see you gypsy, beggin' on my bended knees,
   That man's put something on me, oh take it off of me, please.

3. It starts at my forehead and goes clean down to my toes.
   It starts at my forehead and goes clean down to my toes,
   Oh, how I'm sufferin' gypsy, nobody but the good Lawd knows.

4. Gypsy, don't hurt him, fix him for me one more time,
   Oh, don't hurt him gypsy, fix him for me one more time.
   Just make him love me, but, please mam, take him off my mind.

Reckless Blues

Words and Music by
BESSIE SMITH

108

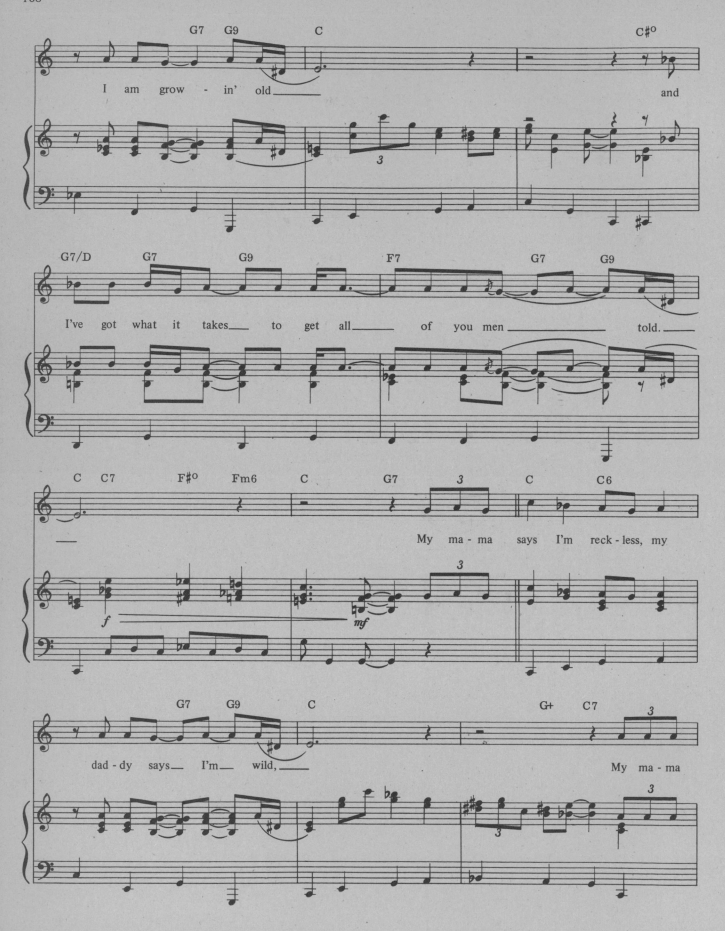

Ma - ma wants some hug - gin'. Darn it pret - ty pa - pa

Ma - ma wants some lov - in' I ___ vow. ___

Darn ___ it pret - ty pa - pa ___

Ma - ma wants some lov - in' right ___ now. ___

My Man Blues

Words and Music by
BESSIE SMITH

(Bessie:) Cla - ra, who was that man I saw you with _____ the oth - er day? _____

(Clara:) Bes - sie that was my smooth black dad - dy

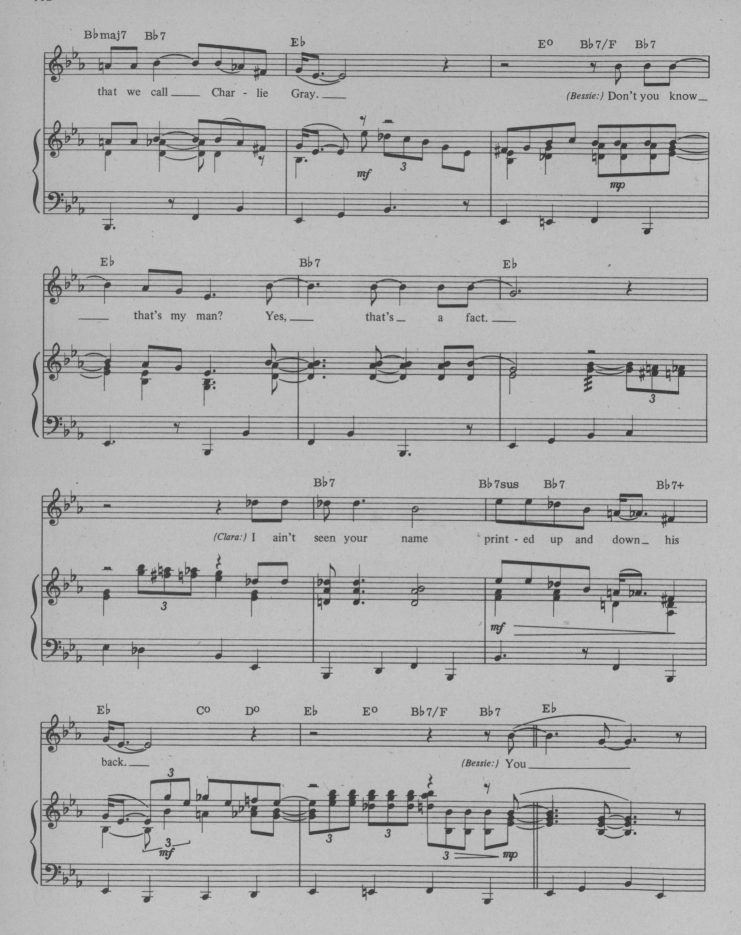

114

Dialogue

(*Bessie:*) Is that you, honey?
(*Charlie:*) Tain't nobody but—Who's back here?
(*Clara:*) It sounds like Charlie.
(*Bessie:*) It is my man, sweet papa Charlie Gray.
(*Clara:*) Your man? How do you git that way?
(*Bessie:*) Now, look here, honey, I been had that man for umpteen year.
(*Clara:*) Child, didn't I turn your damper down?
(*Bessie:*) Yes, Clara, and I've cut you every way but loose!
(*Clara:*) Well, you might as well be get it fixed.
(*Bessie:*) Well, then. . .

Dialogue: (Bessie:) How about it? (Clara:) Suits me! (Bessie:) Suits me! Well, then. . . . . ! ! ! !

Poor Man's Blues

Words and Music by
BESSIE SMITH

Slowly

Mis-ter rich-man, rich-man, o-pen up___ your heart___ and mind.___ Mis-ter rich-man,___ rich-man,_ o-pen up___ your heart_ and mind. Give the

Poor work-ing man's wife is starv-in', your wife is liv-in' like a queen.

2. Please
3. Poor man
4. Now the

2. Please, listen to my pleading, 'cause I can't stand these hard times long.
   Oh, listen to my pleading, can't stand these hard times long.
   They'll make an honest man do things that you know is wrong.

3. Poor man fought all the battles, poor man would fight again today.
   Poor man fought all the battles, poor man would fight again today.
   He would do anything you ask him in the name of the U.S.A.

4. Now the war is over, poor man must live the same as you,
   Now the war is over, poor man must live as same as you,
   If it wasn't for the poor man, mister rich man what would you do?

Hard Time Blues

Words and Music by
BESSIE SMITH

122

123

'Tain't Nobody's Biz-Ness If I Do

Words and Music by
PORTER GRAINGER
and **EVERETT ROBINS**

Slow Blues

Verse: F   A7/E   Dm   A7

There ain't noth-in' I can do or noth-in' I can say___

D7/F#   Am/E D7 Am7   D7   Gm   D7

that folks don't crit - i - cize   me;

Gm   D7   G7   Dm/A G7/B

but I'm go-ing to do just as___ I want___ to an - y - way,

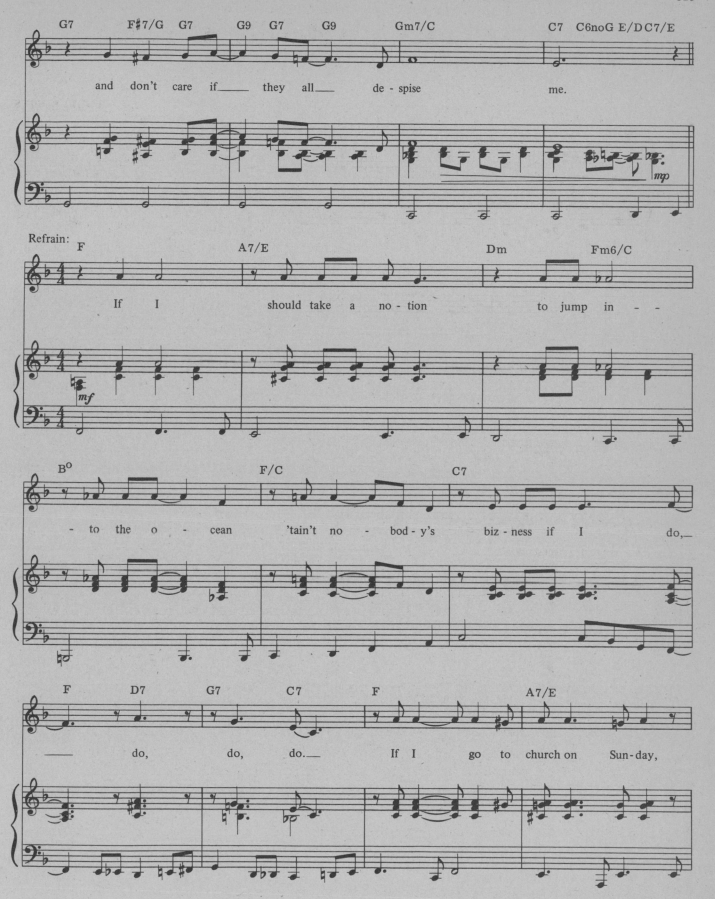

126

128

Cake Walking Babies From Home

Words and Music by
**CHRIS SMITH,
HENRY TROY** and
CLARENCE WILLIAMS

130

Gimme A Pigfoot

Words and Music by
WESLEY WILSON

138

Gulf Coast Blues

Words and Music by
CLARENCE WILLIAMS

Refrain:

Index and Discography

Bessie Smith's total recorded output is available on five two-record albums in the current Columbia catalogue. The following discography lists the thirty songs contained in this book, giving the date of the original recording and catalogue number of the reissue album containing the song. For further reference, the albums are entitled as follows:

GP 33   "The World's Greatest Blues Singer"
G 30126   "Any Woman's Blues"
G 30450   "Empty Bed Blues"
G 30818   "The Empress"
G 31093   "Nobody's Blues But Mine"

An important part of Bessie Smith's artistry was her ability to turn each song into a personal statement, bending the melody and altering the lyrics to suit her phrasing. Whether she added one word or a whole verse, the result was usually an improvement, but there were times when her changes were simply due to her misinterpretation of a lyric as in *Yellow Dog Blues* (not included in this collection) where W. C. Handy's line

"Everywhere that Uncle Sam has a rural delivery" becomes "Everywhere that Uncle Sam is the ruler of delivery."

In order to capture as much of the true spirit of Bessie Smith's music as the printed page will allow, the thirty selections in this collection have been transcribed from Bessie's recorded renditions rather than taken from the original sheet music.